Ski with Peyton

Ski with Peyton

Mike Peyton

Fernhurst Books

First published 1985 by
Fernhurst Books, 13 Fernhurst Road, London SW6 7JN

ISBN 0 906754 21 6

Composition by A&G Phototypesetters, Knaphill
Printed by Hartnoll Print, Bodmin

To the members of the Maldon Little Ski Club

Mike Peyton was cajoled into skiing late in life when someone in a skiing party dropped out and willy-nilly he went to make the numbers up. He is still trying to work out whether it was for better or for worse. He considers the ideal way of finding out would be to have enough money to spend a whole winter skiing, when he would either get it out of his system or perfect his parallels.

9

"We're over the car park . . . you've left the side lights on."

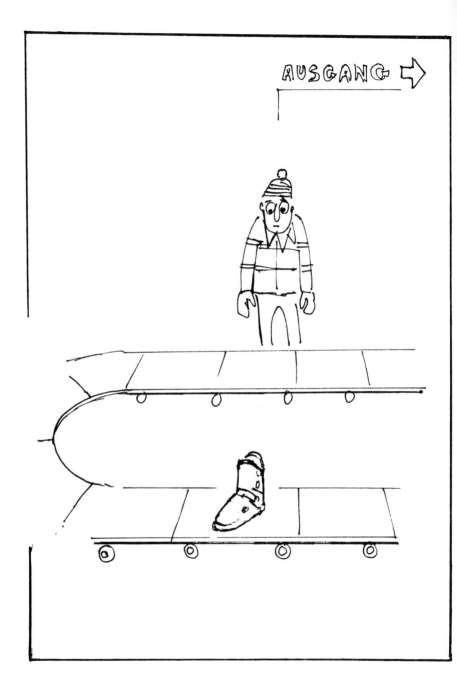

"I appreciate the economies, but never again."

"I wonder what the queue for the lifts will be like."

"Thought he could overtake the whole queue, did he?"

17

"... Captain Morgan and the crew hope you enjoyed your flight,
and wish you a pleasant holiday."

"Every winter we get some."

"It's your Christmas present, Gran. Can I borrow them?"

"Darling . . . I've left the photos at the hotel."

"You've broken it."

"I bet *you* don't know the first thing about maritime law."

"Careful here. It's a black poma."

27

"I always ski better after lunch."

"There you are – what did I tell you?"

"Don't move!"

33

Skiing the bumps – 1

"It should be an interesting insurance claim."

One of the hazards of off-piste skiing . . .

"Of course it's strong enough. Just tie the car keys on it."

"Next kid that jumps the queue . . ."

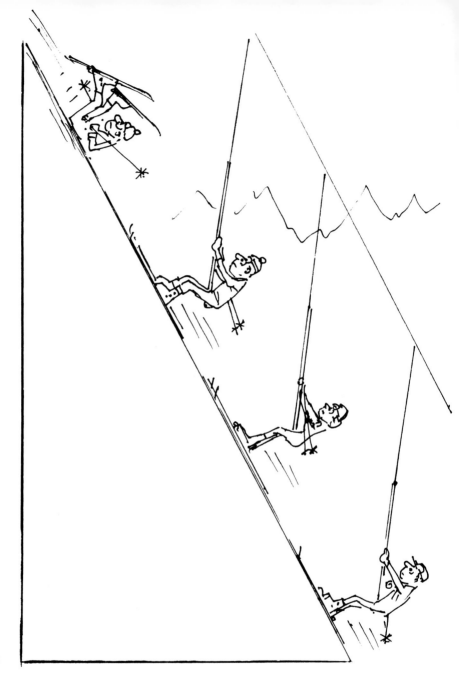

41

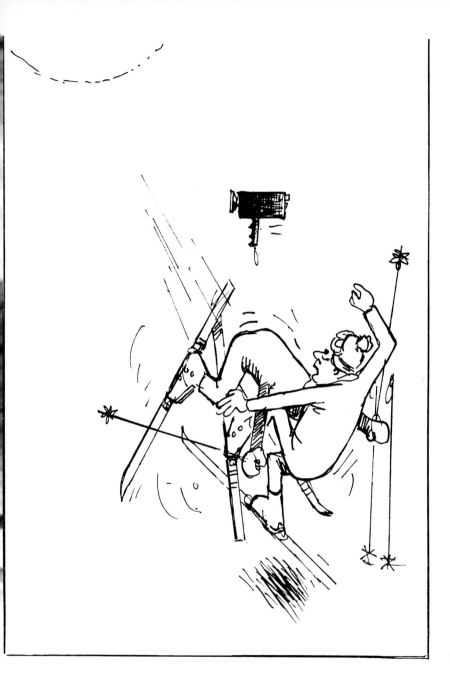

43

"He did it in the chalet — arm wrestling."

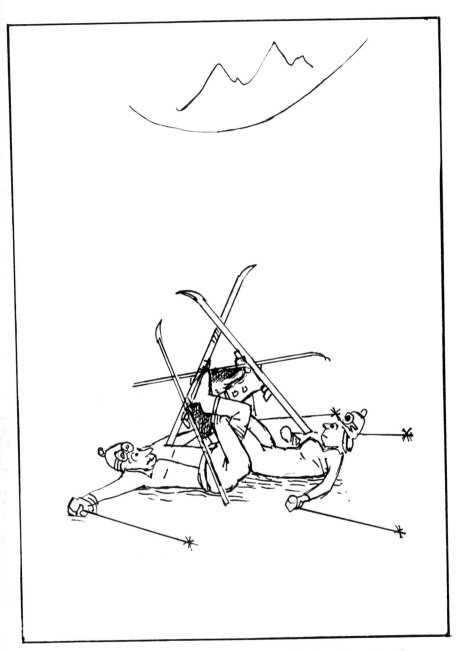

"No good? OK, this time lift your right foot while I twist my ski . . ."

"It will be John. He loves skiing back to the chalet."

"Careful – this bit is black."

51

"I know I had my ski pass with me . . ."

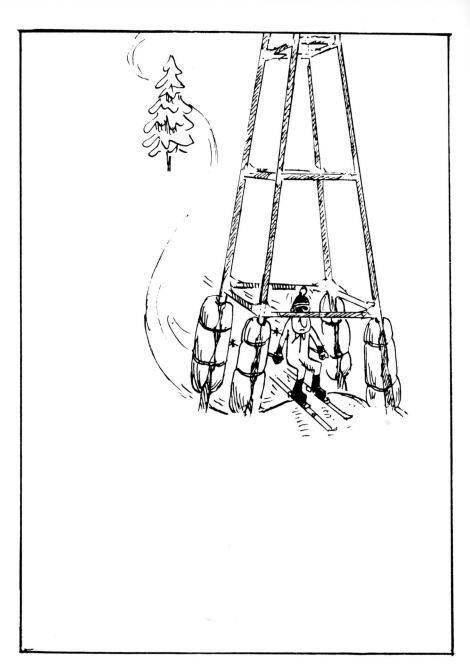

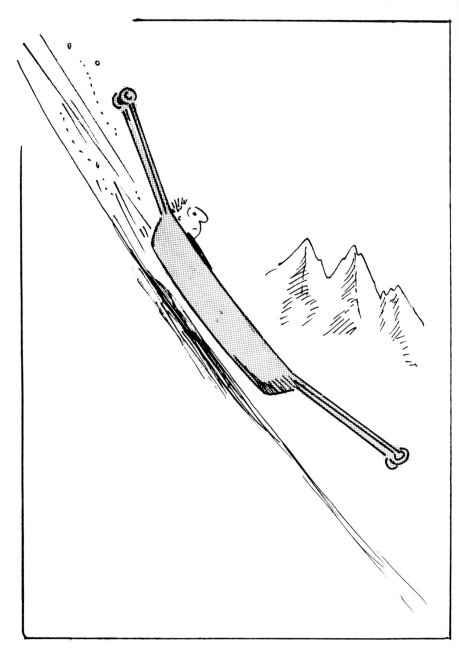

Skiing the bumps – 2

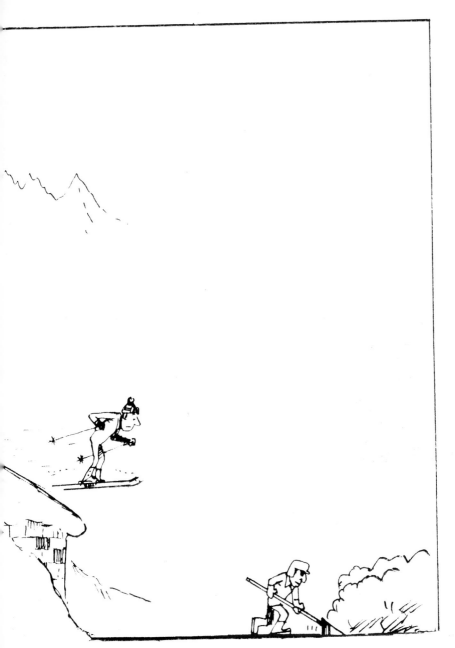

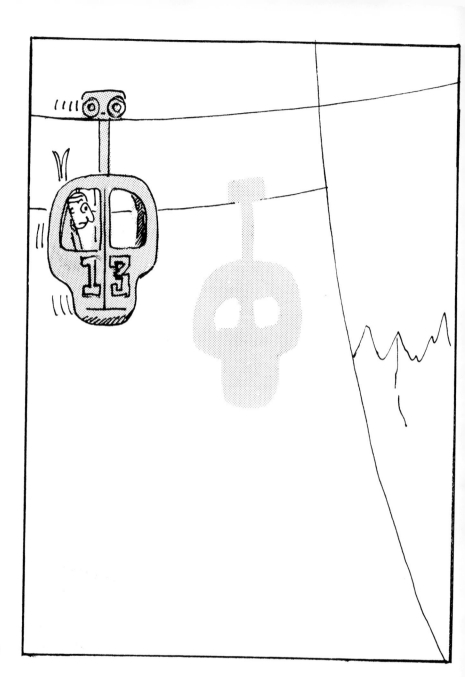

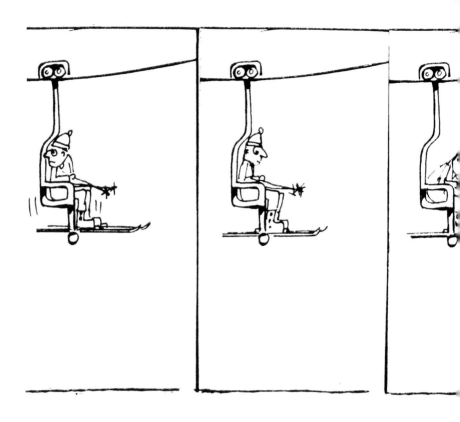

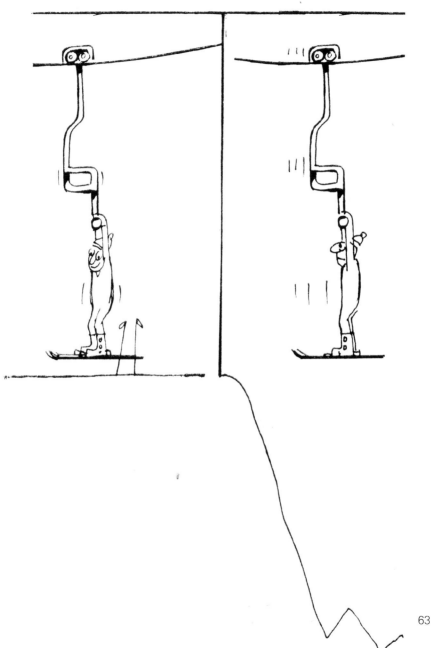

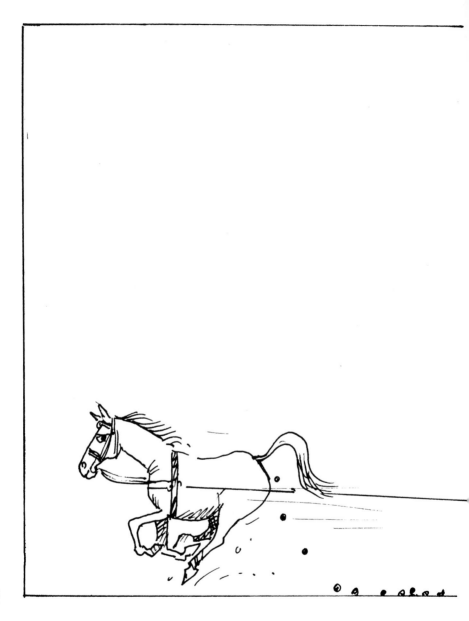

64

66

"I'll see you at the bottom, darling."

67

"It's OK. There are tracks going down."

The disadvantage of a long lunch . . .

"If you think this is green, you must be colour blind."

"You're back early. No snow?"

71

"Come on – only the first two hundred metres are black."

Skiing the bumps – 3

Skiing the bumps – 4

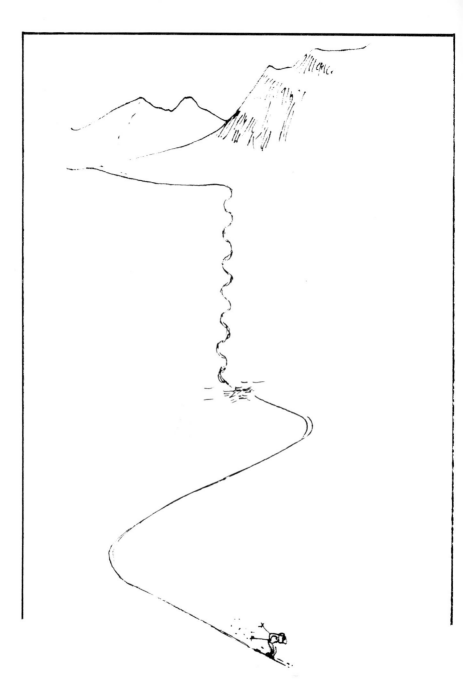

74

The effect of an audience . . .

"It's green."

"What comes after 'Our Father, Who art in Heaven'?"

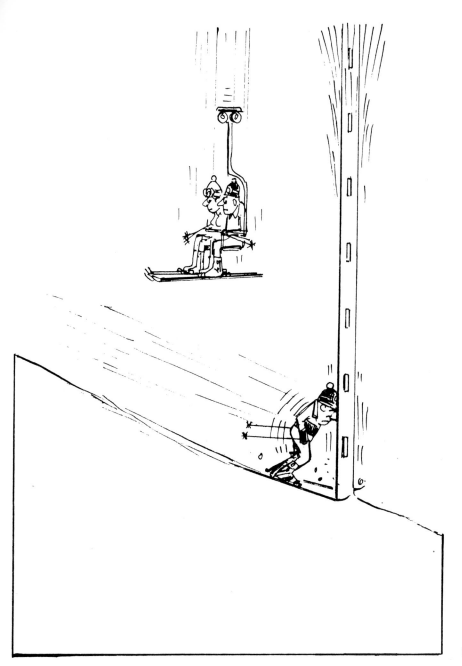

"It's simple: face down the hill, skis parallel, knees bent . . ."

"*That's* what I call body language."

"That couple I shared a bubble with thought I was a foreigner and
were talking about . . ."

"Those are John's boots. I wonder where he is?"

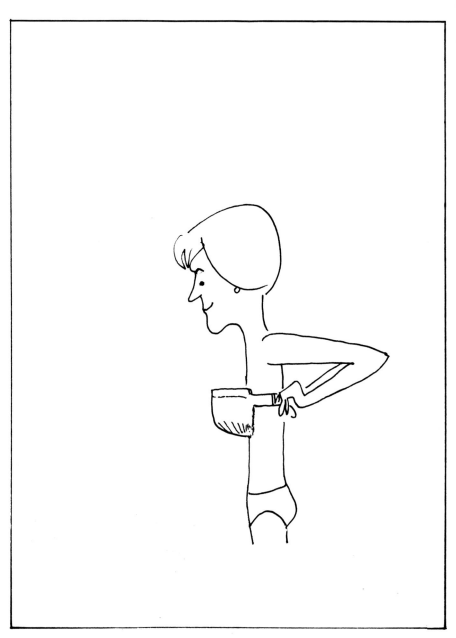

Another use for the 'bum bag'.

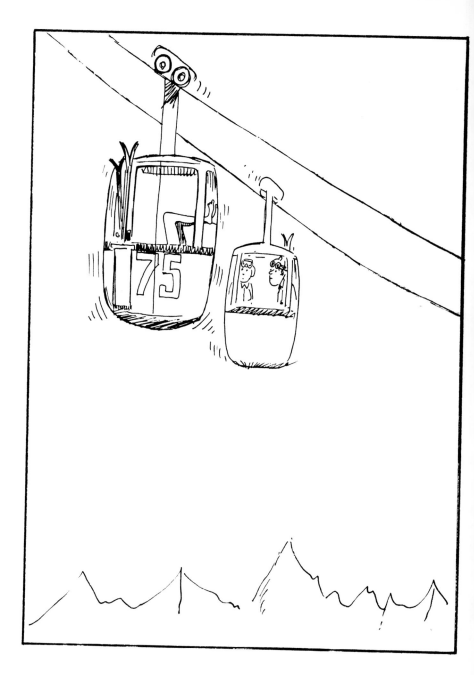

"Put out the light, darling – it's more romantic."

"It's one way of saving a table, I suppose."